CW00338306

This paperback edition published simultaneously in 1992 by Exley
Publications Ltd. in Great Britain, and Exley Giftbooks in the USA.
First hardback edition published in Great Britain in 1987 by Exley
Publications Ltd.

Reprinted 1992 and 1993 (twice)

Copyright © Bill Stott, 1987

ISBN 1-85015-364-7

Printed in Spain by Grafo S.A., Bilbao.

Exley Publications Ltd, 16 Chalk Hill, Watford, Herts WD1 4BN,
United Kingdom.
Exley Giftbooks, 359 East Main Street, Suite 3D, Mount Kisco,
NY 10549, USA.

the CRAZY world of MARRIAGE

Cartoons by Bill Stott

EXLEY

MT. KISCO, NEW YORK • WATFORD, UK

"*Psst! It's still not too late to make a break for it ...*"

"A second honeymoon? Sure, with whom?"

"It might make the world go round but it doesn't make it any tidier!"

"Run away with my wife if you like, but if you value
socks in pairs – forget it!"

"Say you love me."

"*You love me.*"

"Well, if you haven't seen this show before, how come you rustle your paper in all the good bits?"

"You don't understand. I think Madonna's fantastic, ultimately sexy, amazing – a goddess – but I married you."

"Sorry about that, darling, I didn't want to miss the goal. You were saying something about having an affair ...?"

"*Done? I haven't done anything!*"

"We had this room on our first honeymoon ... Look, Paul, there's the very window-seat where you sang Will you love me tomorrow?"

"Why am I on the floor? Last night I tied the duvet to my big toe to stop you stealing it all. You're stronger than I thought."

"Well, there's nothing on TV and I feel like a good laugh. Why don't we get the wedding photos out?"

"I see he's got his Dad's hair ..."

"What do you mean if *I* was the only girl in the world?"

"And when he does come to the supermarket, he's no help."

"*Right, I've got my eyes closed. I just hope you haven't bought anything exotic this time – I can't abide your showy presents.*"

"You do as you're told, young man, or your mother and I will more than likely have an argument."

"*Ease off, Dennis – these people are going to think we're not married.*"

"*I'm just trying to imagine what you'll look like when you're 50, just in case I'm still married to you by then ...*"

"The TV is broken. What is it to be – an argument
or an early night?"

"How come you can shave and wear a tie to go to that office you hate so much, but not when you spend the weekend with me?"

"You really hate football, don't you?"

"I hate it when they take up a sport to be near you and turn out to be good at it."

"I don't love you after all. It turned out to be
chronic indigestion .. "

"Okay, there's something wrong isn't there? I know the signs ..."

"You're not going to be masterful, are you? You always put your back out when you're masterful."

"*Furthermore I also promise to avoid such terms as
'the wife', 'her' or 'my better half'.*"

"I see the Framlinghams had another fight."

"For heaven's sake, how many times have I told you about calling me at work?"

"He thinks I love him for his come-to-bed eyes. Actually I'm crazy about the way he can't put shelves up."

"Sorry darling – you were saying something about how I don't notice you any more …?"

"Aah! A stiff breeze, a willing boat and the woman I love ...
Happy, darling?"

"My but you're magnificent when you're angry!"

"I said 'Why don't you do something for me you haven't done in years?' He tried a headstand ..."

"... just cause or impediment why ..."

"*Just because I can't remember what we were fighting about, doesn't mean I've forgiven you ...*"

"And the Lord have mercy on your soul. Ooops, turned over two pages there!"

"You want something to drive him mad? The effect or the bill?"

"Throw in another pig and I'll take her off your hands."

"You haven't a romantic bone in your body. Why can't you just ignore the greenfly?"

"Of course I'd really like to make it legal, but how do we know he's a real priest?"

"Casserole? Again?"

"The 'better' was okay while it lasted, but the 'worse' was really bad!"

"See his eyes flicker? You'd swear he understood
every word I said!"

"Okay, a truck smashed into our bedroom. But admit it – just for a second you thought the earth moved!"

"It's over then?"

"Hey Doreen – the guy on this TV counseling show just took a call from some woman who claims she hasn't had a meaningful conversation with her husband in 16 years ... Doreen?"

"I know I said it
with music in Majorca;
but this is not Majorca,
I'm freezing and there's
a policeman coming."

"*You may be a mediocre lover, but nobody scratches a back like you do!*"

"You might think it's full of olde worlde charm, but I'll tell you – after an hour every night for the last 23 years, maybe you'd find it a little tedious."

"I wish my folks were like yours and hated pop music ..."

"*Ok, ok, you win. Your paper-hanging is better than mine.*"

"*Get back on your pedestal instantly, woman.*"

"It's my turn to have the headache."

"The old fool insisted on an anniversary waltz – and locked solid!"

"Of course the life insurance is paid up ... why?"

"*You romantic old thing, you!*"

"That ideal man you sorted out for me? It's worn out.
Got any more?"

"Yes, I've come back – but only because Hugo can't settle
at my mother's."

"So this big mean-looking kid walks up and says 'Gimme the bag'.
And Gerry says 'Okay punk, beat it', didn't you Gerry?"

"*Does the best man have the safety pin?*"

"No problem, officer – it's just foreplay!"

"Sorry officer, but this was where it all started.
The first time this was a cornfield."

"George! Stop telling my joke."

"Well I'm glad it's not _my_ husband making a fool of himself!"

"*And that's the Hopkinsons – they have some really good fights.*"

"No dear ... Yes dear ... Pick your mother up? Yes dear ...
Mow the lawn? Yes dear ... No dear ..."

"Last week they promised to pay me a fine each time they forgot to put something away. By now, I could afford a new video!"

"*But I do still love you. It's just your clothes, politics, conversation and habits I want you to change.*"

"Wait a minute – we agreed. Tuesday is my day
to moan about the office!"

"He gave me the best years of his life. As it happened they weren't fantastic, just the best he could do."

Books in the "Crazy World" series

($4.99 £2.99 paperback)

The Crazy World of Aerobics (Bill Stott)
The Crazy World of Cats (Bill Stott)
The Crazy World of Cricket (Bill Stott)
The Crazy World of Gardening (Bill Stott)
The Crazy World of Golf (Mike Scott)
The Crazy World of the Greens (Barry Knowles)
The Crazy World of The Handyman (Roland Fiddy)
The Crazy World of Hospitals (Bill Stott)
The Crazy World of Housework (Bill Stott)
The Crazy World of Learning (Bill Stott)
The Crazy World of Love (Roland Fiddy)
The Crazy World of Marriage (Bill Stott)
The Crazy World of The Office (Bill Stott)
The Crazy World of Photography (Bill Stott)
The Crazy World of Rugby (Bill Stott)
The Crazy World of Sailing (Peter Rigby)
The Crazy World of Sex (David Pye)

Books in the "Mini Joke Book" series

($6.99 £3.99 hardback)

These attractive 64 page mini joke books are illustrated throughout by Bill Stott.

A Binge of Diet Jokes
A Bouquet of Wedding Jokes
A Feast of After Dinner Jokes
A Knockout of Sports Jokes
A Portfolio of Business Jokes
A Round of Golf Jokes
A Romp of Naughty Jokes
A Spread of Over-40s Jokes
A Tankful of Motoring Jokes

Books in the "Fanatics" series

($4.99 £2.99 paperback)

The **Fanatic's Guides** are perfect presents for everyone with a hobby that has got out of hand. Eighty pages of hilarious black and white cartoons by Roland Fiddy.

The Fanatic's Guide to the Bed
The Fanatic's Guide to Cats
The Fanatic's Guide to Computers
The Fanatic's Guide to Dads
The Fanatic's Guide to Diets
The Fanatic's Guide to Dogs
The Fanatic's Guide to Husbands
The Fanatic's Guide to Money
The Fanatic's Guide to Sex
The Fanatic's Guide to Skiing

Books in the "Victim's Guide" series

($4.99 £2.99 paperback)

Award winning cartoonist Roland Fiddy sees the funny side to life's phobias, nightmares and catastrophes.

The Victim's Guide to the Dentist
The Victim's Guide to the Doctor
The Victim's Guide to Middle Age

Great Britain: Order these super books from your local bookseller or from Exley Publications Ltd, 16 Chalk Hill, Watford, Herts WD1 4BN. (Please send £1.30 to cover postage and packing on 1 book, £2.60 on 2 or more books.)